Usborne
Speaking English Activity Book

Illustrated by Marcella Grassi
Words by Mairi Mackinnon. Edited by Felicity Brooks
Designed by Meg Dobbie

How to say the English words
You can hear all the English phrases in this book, read by a native English speaker, at the Usborne Quicklinks website. Just go to **www.usborne.com/quicklinks** and enter the keywords **speaking english**.

Find these in the big picture.

a boy with a bicycle

a dog

this girl

this bag

In the park

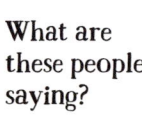

What are these people saying?

How many can you see in the big picture?

birds

backpacks

wheels

ducks

butterflies

Who is saying ..?

Hello. What's your name?

Is your mum here?

That's my dad.

Find these people in the big picture.

the bride

the groom

a waiter

a photographer

At a wedding

Which one do you like best?

What are they saying?

At the café

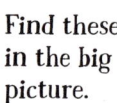 tea
 cake
 coffee
 sandwich

Find these in the big picture.

What are they saying?

In the town

- Are you all right?
- I've lost my parents.
- Don't worry, we'll find them.
- I'm sorry, I don't understand.
- Can you say that again?
- Careful!
- Sorry!
- Can I help you?
- I don't speak English very well.
- Here, sit down.
- I'm not feeling well.
- Would you like some water?

Who is saying..?

- Can I help you?
- Are you all right?
- Would you like some water?

At school

True or false?

This boy has plans for the weekend.

This boy loves skateboarding.

This girl is going to the show.

This girl can play tennis.

Which do *you* like doing?

reading

playing tennis

skateboarding

Find these in the big picture.

a clock

a plant

a map

a computer

Do you have them in *your* school?

In the classroom

"Sorry I'm late."

"This is difficult."

"What are we doing next?"

"I don't know. Ask the teacher."

"Wait a minute. I'll look it up."

"Where's your book?"

"I left it at home."

"How do you say 'répéter' in English?"

Find someone who...

...has this book open.

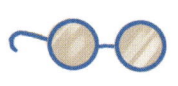

...wears these glasses.

...has this lunch box.

How many can you find in the big picture?

bags

pens

pictures

children

Who is saying..? Good morning. Can I borrow your pen? Sorry I'm late.

Find these in the big picture.

a hat

some sunglasses

a pink t-shirt

a green mat

yellow sandals

At the seaside

Can I help you?

Do you sell postcards?

Yes, of course.

Do you like this t-shirt?

I prefer that one.

Can I have an ice cream?

What are they saying?

Find another one...

...like this, but green.

...like this, but with pink stripes.

...like this, but yellow.

...like this, but blue.

...like this, but chocolate and strawberry.

These are the answers. What are the questions?

Yes, of course.

I prefer that one.

They're 5.99.

Which would *you* like to do?

Go on the rollercoaster.

Ride in the teacups.

Go down the slide.

Eat some candyfloss.

What are they saying?

At the funfair

Are you having fun

This ride is boring. Let's try that one.

I'm not sure. I'm nervous.

Look what I won.

Oh, you are lucky!

What's the matter?

OK, let's go home

I'm tired.

True or false?

This girl is hungry.

This boy is tired.

This boy is ready.

This girl is lucky.

Find the complete sentences.

This ride...

What's..?

I need...

Look at both pictures. Where do you go to...

...show your passport?

...collect your bags?

At the airport

...buy a train ticket?

...go to the toilet?

At the station

Who is saying..?

- I'm afraid I have to go now.
- I need to change some money.
- Thanks for everything.